THE COMPLETE PIANO PLAYI
BOOK 5

'By the end of this book you will
be playing with new power and confidence,
and you will be playing 20 popular songs,
including: *Song For Guy, Can't Smile Without You,
The Entertainer,* and *The Theme from E.T.*'

Kenneth Baker

Kenneth Baker

Wise Publications
London/New York/Paris/Sydney/Copenhagen/Madrid

Exclusive Distributors:
Music Sales Limited
8/9 Frith Street, London W1V 5TZ, England.
Music Sales Pty Limited
120 Rothschild Avenue, Rosebery, NSW 2018, Australia.

This book © Copyright 1984, 1993 by
Wise Publications
ISBN 0-7119-0435-9
Order No. AM34869

Designed by Howard Brown
Photography by Peter Wood
Music arranged by Kenneth Baker

Music Sales' complete catalogue describes thousands of titles and
is available in full colour sections by subject, direct from Music Sales Limited.
Please state your areas of interest and send a cheque/postal order for
£1.50 for postage to: Music Sales Limited, Newmarket Road,
Bury St. Edmunds, Suffolk IP33 3YB.

Your Guarantee of Quality
As publishers, we strive to produce every book to the highest
commercial standards. The music has been freshly engraved and the
book has been carefully designed to minimise awkward page turns
and to make playing from it a real pleasure.
Particular care has been given to specifying acid-free, neutral-sized
paper made from pulps which have not been elemental
chlorine bleached. This pulp is from farmed sustainable forests
and was produced with special regard for the environment.
Throughout, the printing and binding have been planned to ensure
a sturdy, attractive publication which should give years of enjoyment.
If your copy fails to meet our high standards, please inform us and
we will gladly replace it.

Printed in the United Kingdom by
Halstan & Co Limited, Amersham, Buckinghamshire.

CONTENTS

ABOUT THIS BOOK

In this book you will be introduced to many new skills and techniques, which will take you further along the path to becoming a complete piano player. At the same time, the skills you have already acquired from the first four books will be reinforced.

You will learn more about phrasing, and how **dynamics** in music can transform your playing to a remarkable degree. Four new keys are introduced and you will make the acquaintance of $\frac{12}{8}$, $\frac{3}{8}$, and the rare, but interesting, $\frac{3}{2}$ time. New left hand techniques are dealt with; in fact, your left hand, generally, will be strengthened through being able to handle jumps, wide broken chords and octave playing.

As usual, all lessons in this book are based on some of the most popular songs ever written, as well as on famous light classical pieces. In all you will add twenty outstanding new songs to your ever growing repertoire.

WRIST STACCATO AGAIN

We begin Book Five with a lively little number called *Birdie Song*.

The Chorus of this piece is a further exercise in 'wrist staccato' for the right hand (look again at Book Two, page 44). Let the hand 'bounce' freely from the wrist joint.

BIRDIE SONG/BIRDIE DANCE

Words & Music: Werner Thomas & Terry Rendall

PLAYING IN 12/8 TIME

2

When a piece of music has a time signature of 12/8 it means that there are twelve quavers, or their equivalent, per bar.

As in 6/8 Time (see Book Three, page 16), the quavers are grouped into 'threes':

Example 1

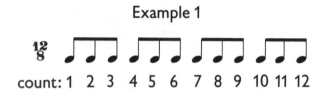

count: 1 2 3 4 5 6 7 8 9 10 11 12

A more typical 12/8 bar might look like this:

Example 2

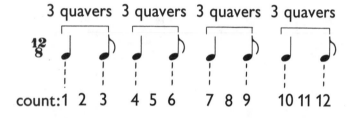

count: 1 2 3 4 5 6 7 8 9 10 11 12

Although it is sometimes desirable to count the full twelve quavers in a bar (for instance, in the early stages of practice, when you are playing the piece very slowly), it is usually simpler to count four dotted crotchets (dotted quarter notes) in a bar:

Example 1

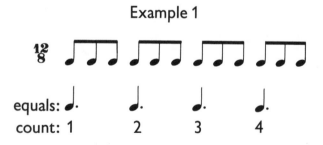

equals:
count: 1 2 3 4

Any subdivisions of the beat that occur can be counted as 'a-and':

Example 1

count: 1 - a -and 2- a -and 3 - a -and 4- a -and

Example 2

12/8

1 -a-and 2-a-and 3-a-and 4-a-and

In Example 1 you play on every beat and every subdivision of the beat; in Example 2 you play on every beat and every 'and' part of the beat. **Remember:** your '1-a-and, 2-a-ands', etc. must be perfectly regular and even, like the ticking of a clock.

With practice you should be able to drop the 'a-and' subdivisions and count only the main beats: '1, 2, 3, 4…'

Your first piece in $\frac{12}{8}$ Time is a traditional American song which has reappeared over the years in various modern arrangements. It's called: *The House Of The Rising Sun.* Here are various ways of 'counting' the melody (which way you choose depends on your stage of practice, and your familiarity with the tune):

THE HOUSE OF THE RISING SUN (Bars 1-4)

(etc.)

Your second piece in $\frac{12}{8}$ Time is *What A Wonderful World* (page 12). This features a typical modern $\frac{12}{8}$ rhythm pattern in the left hand:

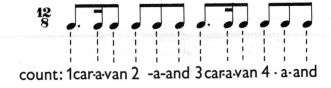

count: 1car·a·van 2 -a-and 3 car·a·van 4 · a·and

Say 'one caravan...' as in normal speech, but be sure to play **only on the syllables shown above.** This should give you the correct sound of this rhythm. Notice that the complete rhythm pattern consists of a 'caravan' group, followed by a simple '2-a-and' group, followed by another 'caravan' group, followed by a simple '4-a-and' group, and so on.

HOUSE OF THE RISING SUN

Traditional

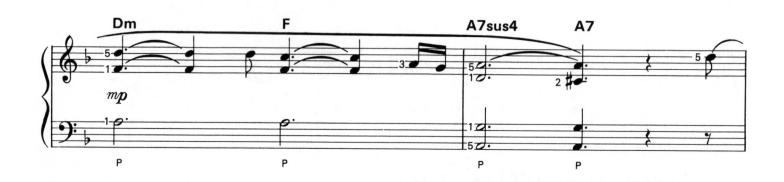

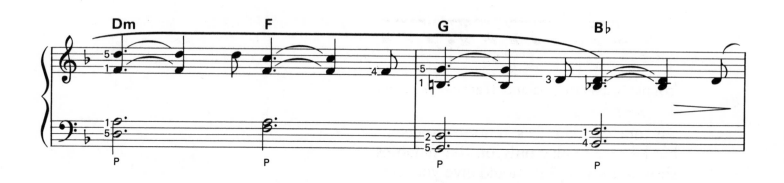

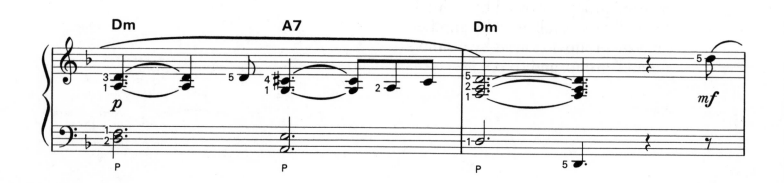

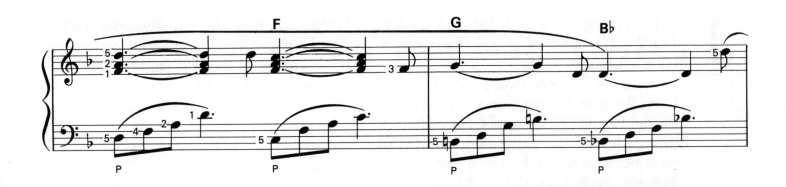

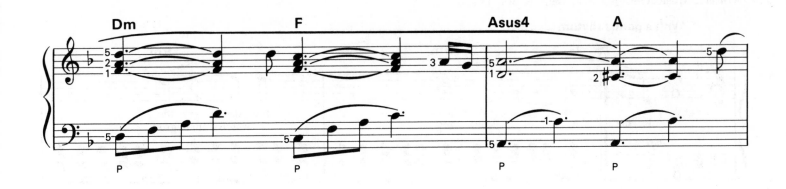

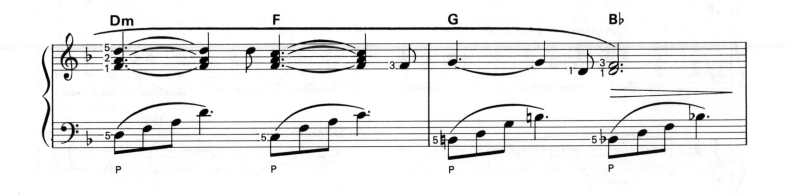

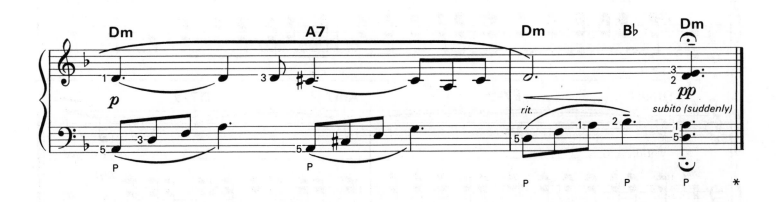

WRIST STACCATO FOR LEFT HAND

3

In the following piece: *What A Wonderful World*, you will be using 'wrist staccato' in your left hand.
Look again at Book Two, page 44. Everything said there about wrist staccato for right hand can be applied equally well to your left hand. Above all don't let your wrist become too tight; let the hand 'bounce' freely from the wrist joint.

Before you play *What A Wonderful World*, turn back to page 9 and read again about the counting of the left hand rhythm patterns in this piece.

WHAT A WONDERFUL WORLD
Words & Music: George David Weiss & Bob Thiele

LEFT HAND OCTAVES

4

In the next two pieces: *Swingin' Shepherd Blues,* and *Yesterday,* you will be playing octaves in your left hand. In *Swingin' Shepherd Blues,* for the sake of simplicity, finger all these octaves (including those on black notes) $\frac{1}{5}$.

Before you start to play, practise the scale of C (and any other scales) in left hand octaves, just to get the feel of the distance (see Book Four, page 37–Right Hand Octaves).

In *Swingin' Shepherd Blues* pay particular attention to the 'phrasing' (staccato, accent, and phrase marks). This piece is another good example of 'syncopation' (see Book Four, page 26).

SWINGIN' SHEPHERD BLUES
Words: Rhoda Roberts and Kenny Jacobson. Music: Moe Koffman

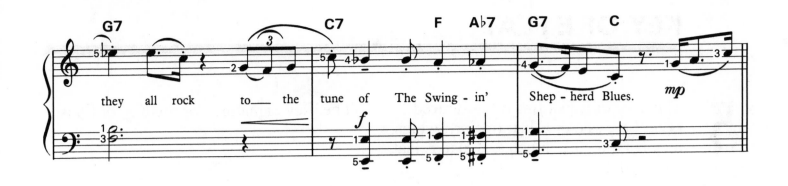

they all rock to___ the tune of The Swing-in' Shep-herd Blues.

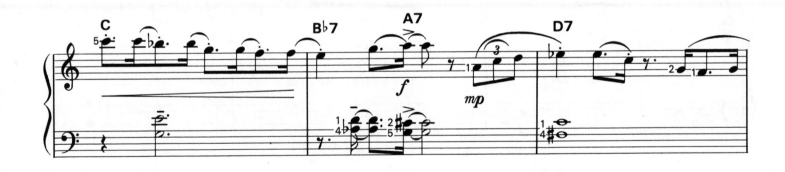

5

The Key of E Flat (major) is derived from the Scale of E Flat (major), which requires three black notes: B Flat, E Flat, and A Flat:

Scale of E♭

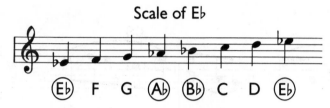

Pieces using this scale predominantly are said to be in the 'Key of E Flat'.

The 'Key Signature' for the Key of E♭ is:

Key of E♭

B Flat, E Flat, A Flat

When you are in this Key you must remember to play all B's, E's, and A's (wherever they might fall on the keyboard) as B Flats, E Flats, and A Flats.

In *Yesterday* you will be playing left hand octaves more or less throughout. On the white note octaves use fingering $\frac{1}{5}$. On the black note octaves use fingering $\frac{1}{4}$ if this comes easily to you, if not, use $\frac{1}{5}$.

YESTERDAY

Words & Music: John Lennon and Paul McCartney

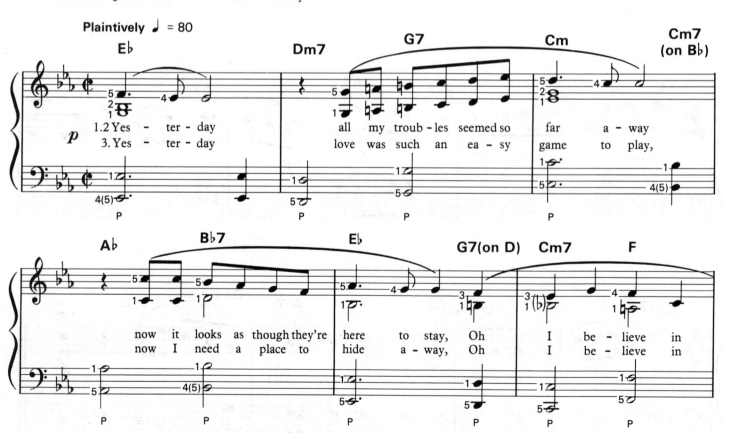

yes - ter - day.
yes - ter - day.
Why she had to go I don't

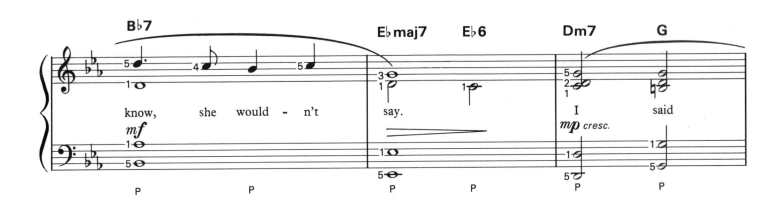

know, she would - n't say. I said

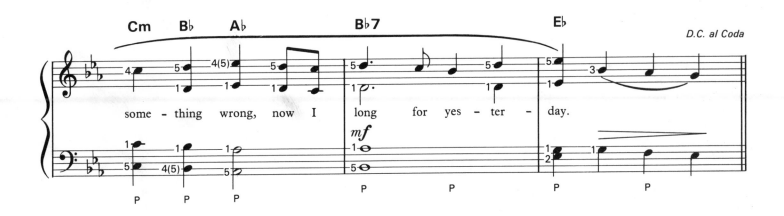

some - thing wrong, now I long for yes - ter - day.

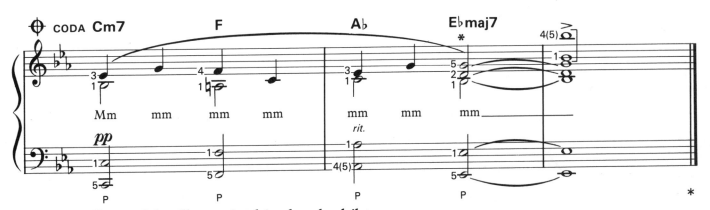

Mm mm mm mm mm mm mm

*The pedal will sustain this chord whilst
the right hand plays the octave B Flat.

DYNAMICS IN MUSIC

Dynamics in music are the 'louds', 'softs', 'crescendos', and the like, which help give the music life.

Your next piece: *Together*, depends for its effect on interesting dynamics. Make the most of the little 'echoes' of the tune (Bars 4, 8, 12, etc.). Play the main parts of the melody

here '*mf*', followed by the echoes '*pp*'. Build to a strong climax in Bars 27 and 28, then taper off to nothing during the last line of the piece, and include a long 'rallentando' (gradual slowing down).

Notice the way the left hand part 'borrows' the Treble Clef for those rather high notes in the 'echoes' bars.

TOGETHER

Words & Music: B.G. De Sylva, Lew Brown & Ray Henderson

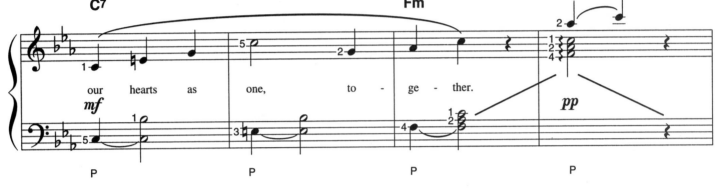

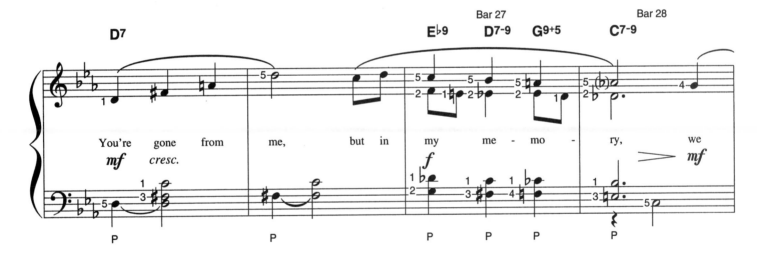

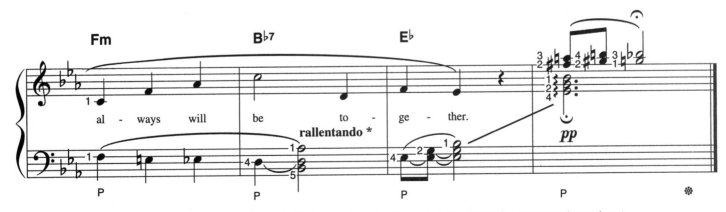

* Rallentando, 'Rall.' for short, means gradually slowing down. A rallentando tends to be more drawn out than a ritenuto.

PHRASING AGAIN

7

Wheels is a playful, cheeky little number, where 'phrasing' is all important.

You will remember from Book Three (page 12) that phrasing is concerned with **how** you play the notes: staccato or legato, with or without an accent, and so on.

In this piece be sure to make the contrast between 'staccato' phrasing in one hand, and 'legato' phrasing in the other. For instance, in Bars 1 and 3, let's hear the 'stabbed' double notes in your left hand contrast with that smooth right hand melody; and in Bar 4, note the first two right hand notes, which are to be played 'staccato', contrasting with the rising left hand figure, which is to be played 'legato'.

WHEELS

Music: Norman Petty. Words: Jimmy Torres & Richard Stephens

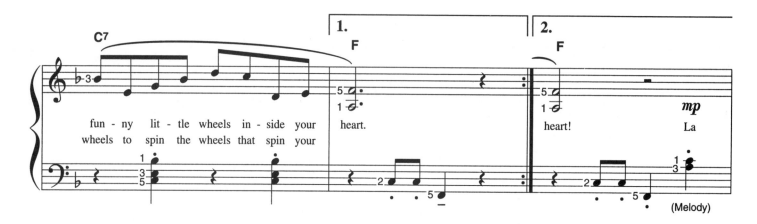

LEFT HAND JUMPS

8

In the next piece the left hand has to make continuous jumps – down for a low note, up for a chord, and so on. You must develop the capacity to glance quickly down at the keyboard to see where you are going, then back to the music without losing your place.

GYMNOPÉDIE No. 1

By Erik Satie

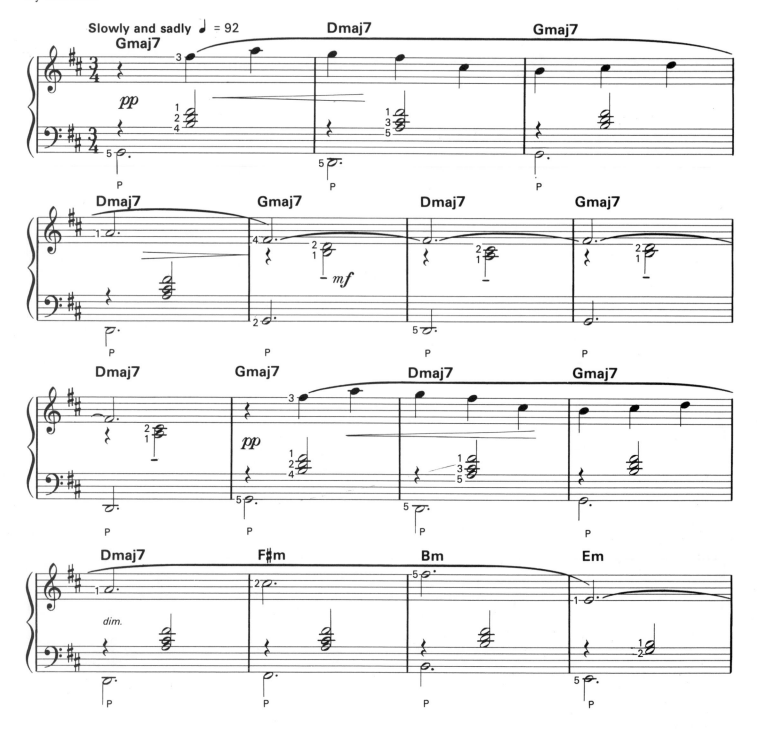

NEW LEFT HAND RHYTHM PATTERN

9

In the first part of *Song For Guy* you will be playing a new left hand rhythm pattern:

This is similar to the Bossa Nova rhythm pattern first given in Book Four (page 44):

The difference in the *Song For Guy* rhythm is that, having played on the 'and' beat, you hold the note down for the rest of the bar.

SONG FOR GUY

By Elton John

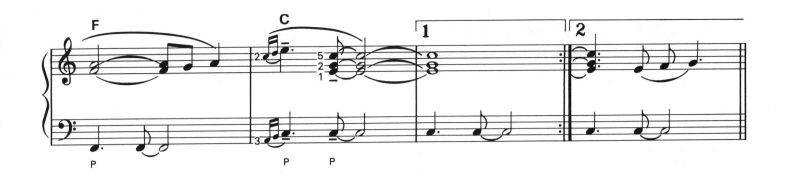

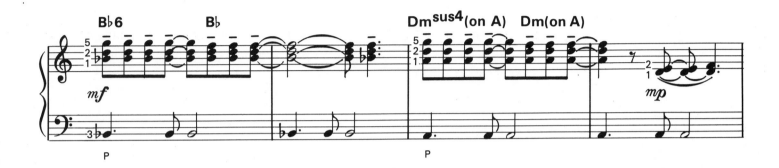

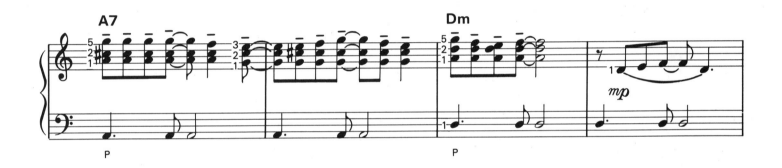

D.C. & Fade on 1st 16 bars

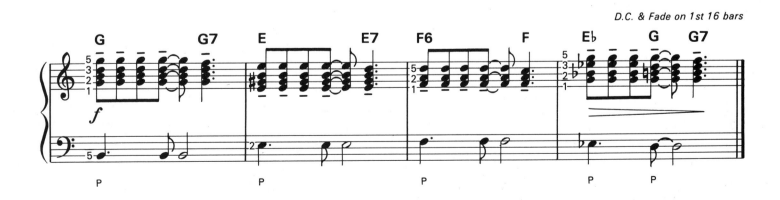

KEY OF C MINOR

10

C Minor is the **relative minor** of 'E Flat Major', both keys requiring three flats: B Flat, E Flat, and A Flat:

The accidentals likely to occur in the Key of C Minor are:

B♮ and A♮

The following piece begins in the Key of C Minor and modulates (i.e. changes Key) at the end to E♭ Major (the **relative major**).

Scale/Key of E♭ (Major)

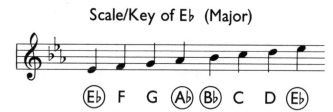

E♭ F G A♭ B♭ C D E♭

Scale/Key of C Minor

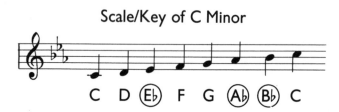

C D E♭ F G A♭ B♭ C

THE SHADOW OF YOUR SMILE

Words: Paul Francis Webster. Music: Johnny Mandel

things you are to me_____ Our wist-ful lit-tle

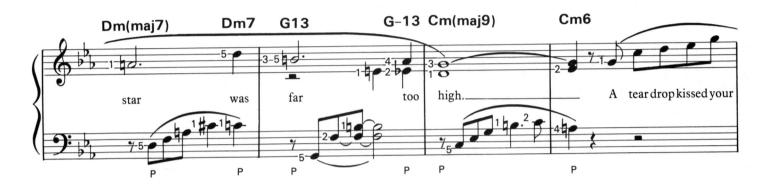

star was far too high. A tear drop kissed your

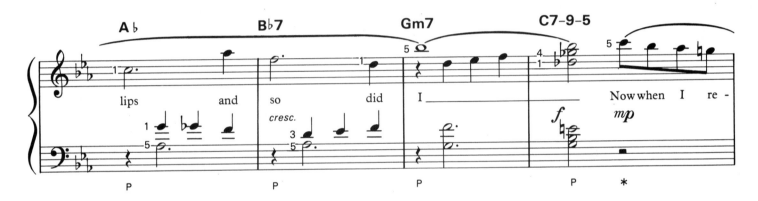

lips and so did I_____ Now when I re-

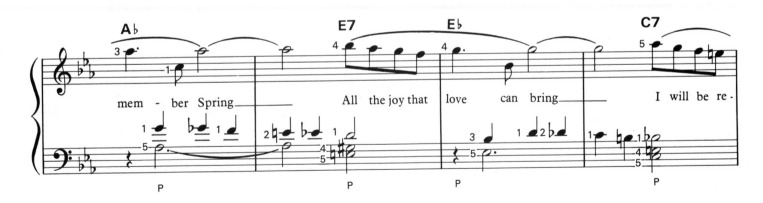

mem - ber Spring All the joy that love can bring I will be re-

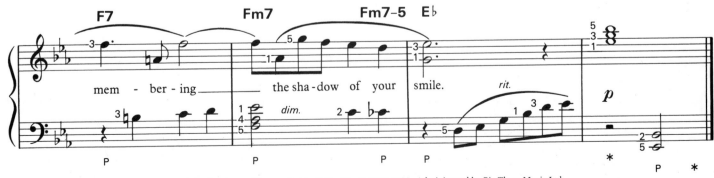

mem - ber - ing_____ the sha-dow of your smile.

TWO TUNES AT ONCE

In Bars 16-22 of the next piece you play fragments of the main theme of *Can't Smile Without You* with your left hand, while your right hand plays a different theme above it. In other words, you play two tunes at once.

Make your left hand slightly louder than your right hand at this point.

Observe the instruction given at the beginning of the piece: 'with a lilt'.

CAN'T SMILE WITHOUT YOU

Words & Music : Chris Arnold, David Martin & Geoff Morrow

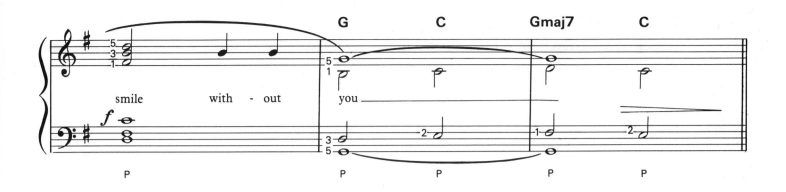

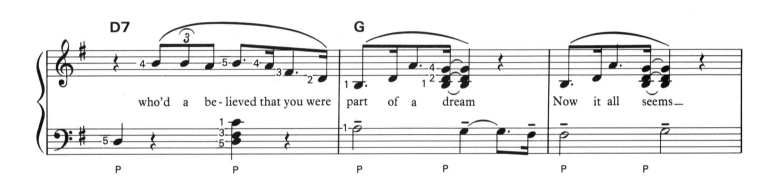

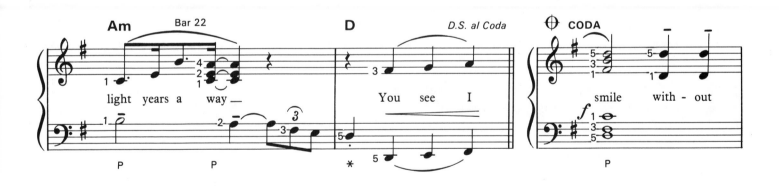

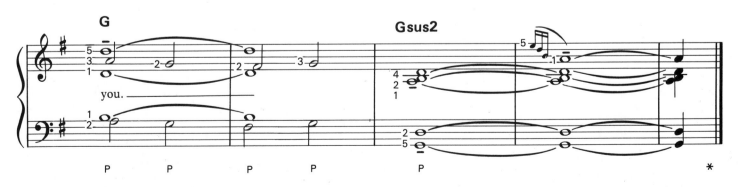

KEY OF A

12

The Key of A (Major) is derived from the Scale of A (Major), which requires three black notes: F Sharp, C Sharp, and G Sharp:

Scale of A

Pieces using this scale predominantly are said to be in the Key of A.

The Key Signature for the key of A is:

Key of A

F sharp, C sharp, G sharp

When you are in this key you must remember to play all F's, C's, and G's (wherever they might fall on the keyboard) as F Sharps, C Sharps, and G Sharps.

SCALE OF A

13

Before you begin *Prelude in A Major*, by Chopin, play through the Scale of A a few times with your right hand. This is to help you feel the 'shape' of the key. Here's the fingering for two octaves:

Scale of A

Notice that your thumb plays every 'A' and every 'D', except for the top 'A', which is played by your little finger (5), for convenience.

It is always useful to play through the scale of a new key, since it helps teach the fingers where the necessary black notes lie.

PRELUDE IN A MAJOR

By Frederik Chopin

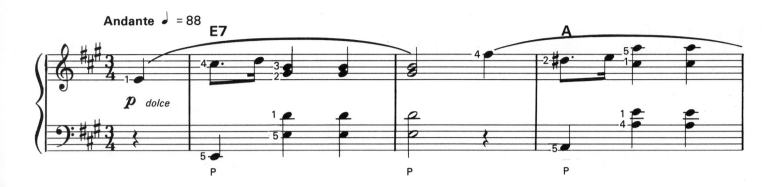

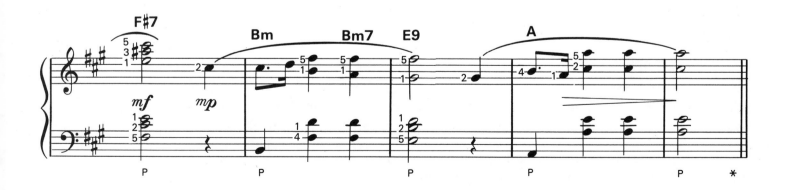

KEY OF A MINOR

14

A Minor is the 'relative minor' key of C Major, in which there are no sharps or flats:

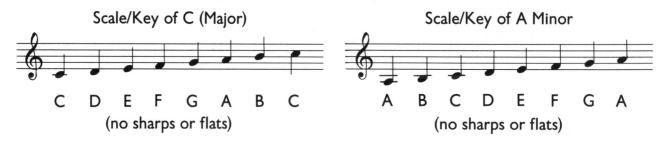

Scale/Key of C (Major)

C D E F G A B C
(no sharps or flats)

Scale/Key of A Minor

A B C D E F G A
(no sharps or flats)

There are two 'accidental' sharps likely to occur in the Key of A Minor. They are:

G♯ and F♯

As it happens, in *Für Elise* (your piece in the Key of A Minor), there is another accidental which keeps appearing:

D♯

This is simply a 'passing note' (see Book Two, page 24), and has no connection with the Scale of A Minor.

⅜ TIME

15

Your next piece, Beethoven's *Für Elise*, is written in ⅜ Time. This means that there are three quavers (three 'eighth' notes), or their equivalent, to the bar:

Example

count: 1 2 3 | 1 2 3 | 1 and 2 and 3 and | 1 2 and 3 and | 1 2 3

⅜ Time is usually chosen in preference to ¾ Time when the piece is of a flowing, running nature, like *Für Elise*.

FÜR ELISE

By: Ludwig Van Beethoven

*High E (see p.36)

A STUDY IN ACCIDENTALS

Your next piece, *What Are You Doing The Rest Of Your Life?*, is in the key of A Minor. The middle section, however, passes through the keys of A Major, Gb Major, and F Major, returning again to the key of A Minor for a repeat of the main theme.

This mixture of keys is the reason for the many accidentals (sharps, flats, and naturals, not in the key signature) which you will find in this piece.

WHAT ARE YOU DOING THE REST OF YOUR LIFE?

Words: Alan & Marilyn Bergman. Music: Michel Legrand

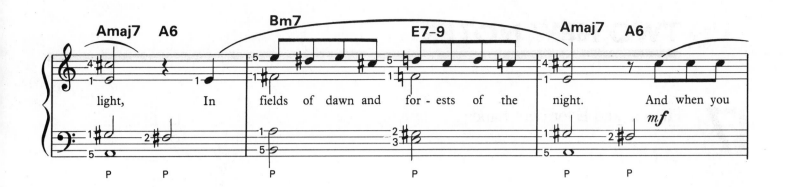

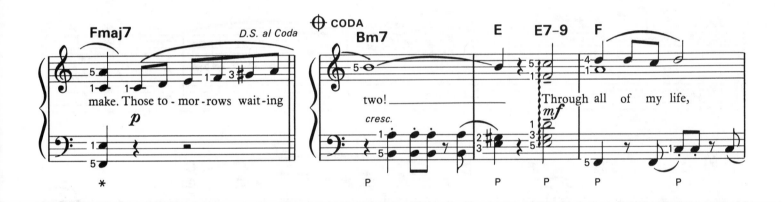

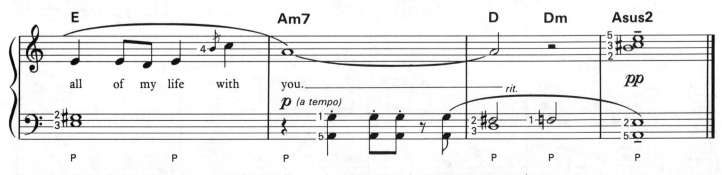

TWO NEW NOTES

High D and E for right hand :

THE ENTERTAINER
By Scott Joplin

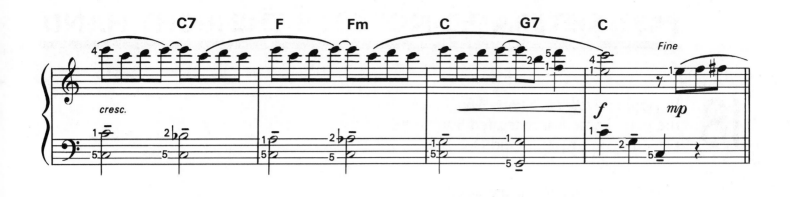

FAST REITERATED NOTES IN THE RIGHT HAND

18

In *With A Little Help From My Friends* there are some fast reiterated 'D's' to be played by your right hand (see Bars 9, 11, and 13).

In such passages it is usual to change the finger on each reiterated note to ensure that the note actually plays again. Here are two exercises for you to practise:

Keep very close to the keys.
Observe the accents.
Make sure that all the notes play.
Gradually speed up.

WITH A LITTLE HELP FROM MY FRIENDS

Words & Music: John Lennon and Paul McCartney

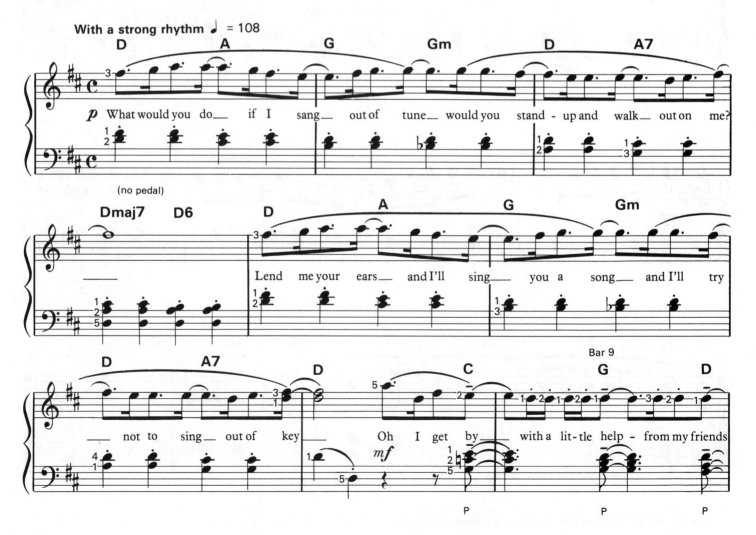

38

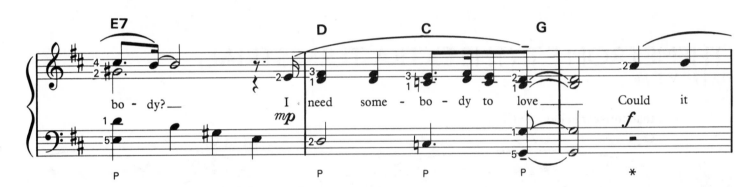

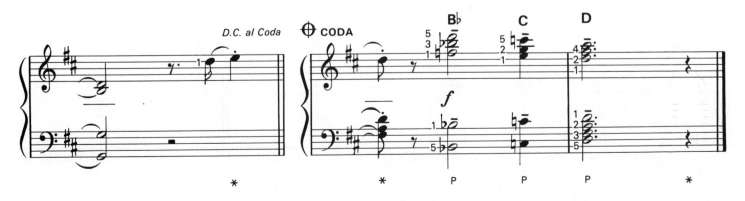

$\frac{3}{2}$ TIME

Your next piece, the *Theme From E.T.*, is written in $\frac{3}{2}$ Time. This means that there are three minims (three 'half' notes), or their equivalent, to the bar:

Example

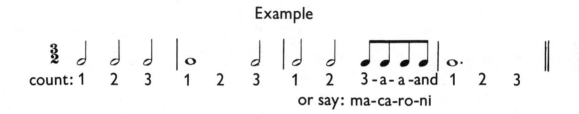

count: 1   2   3   1   2   3   1   2   3 -a- a -and   1   2   3

or say: ma-ca-ro-ni

$\frac{3}{2}$ Time is usually chosen in preference to $\frac{3}{4}$ Time when the piece is slow and drawn out, like the *Theme From E.T.*

THEME FROM E.T. (THE EXTRA-TERRESTRIAL)

By John Williams

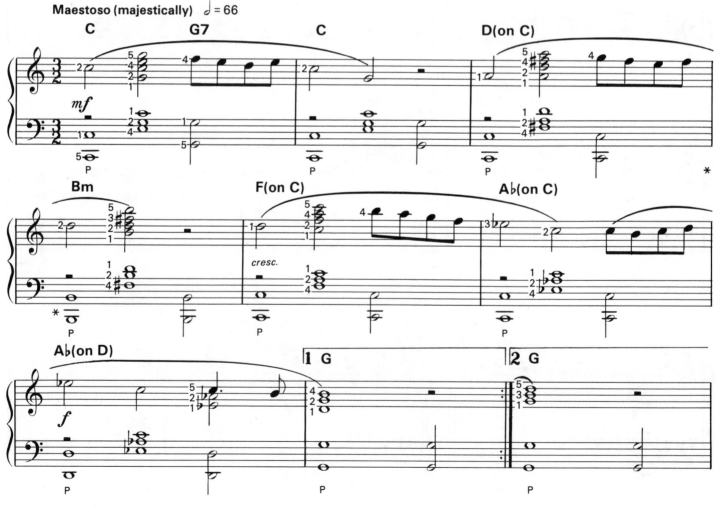

*Low B

40

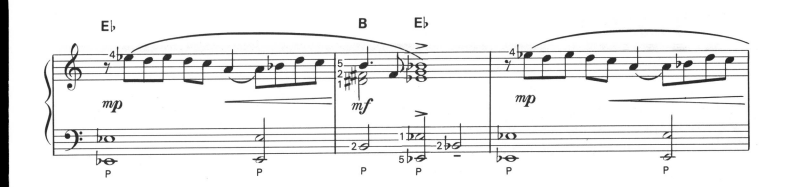

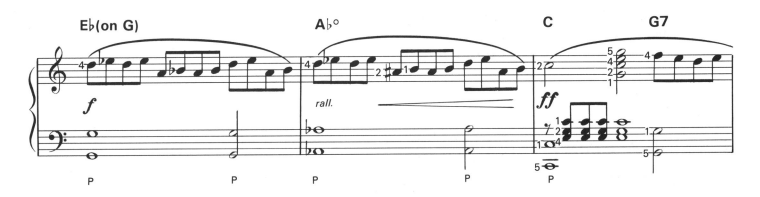

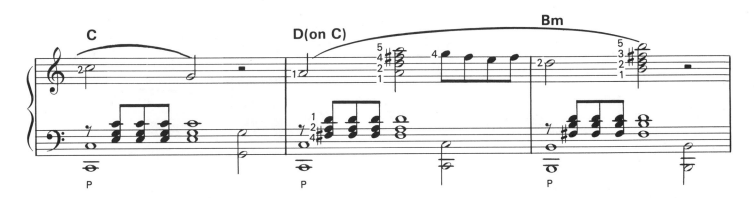

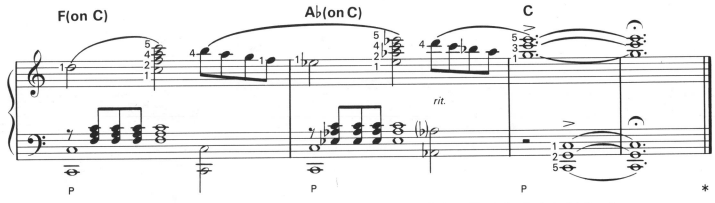

TREMOLO

20

Your next piece: *The Pink Panther Theme*, is an interesting piece of mood music. This comic suspense style theme is greatly enhanced by the use of 'tremolos'.

THE PINK PANTHER THEME

Play the two notes E and B in rapid succession continuously for a bar and a half (six crotchet beats).

Use a rolling action of the wrist on your tremolos rather than finger muscles alone. Do not hold your wrist too tightly.

THE PINK PANTHER THEME

Words & Music: Henry Mancini

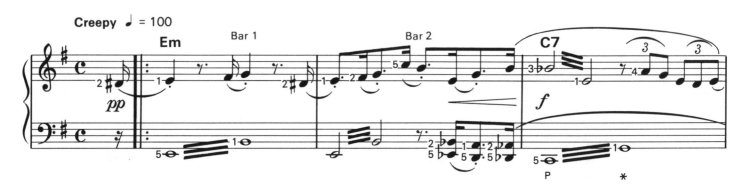

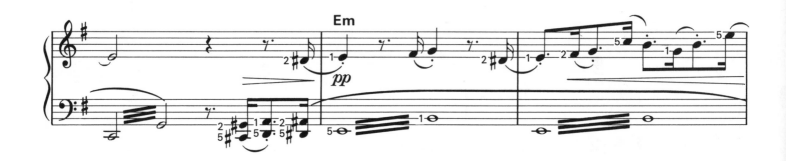

BOTH HANDS HIGH

In the next piece, *Music Box Dancer*, both hands play high on the keyboard in order to simulate a musical box. To avoid using a large number of Ledger Lines to express the notes:

- The left hand is written in Treble Clef throughout.

- The right hand is written normally, but is to be played one octave (eight notes) higher than written.
  This is expressed: 8va.

  Try holding down the Soft Pedal (written: una corda) through this piece: it may improve the musical box effect.

MUSIC BOX DANCER
By Frank Mills

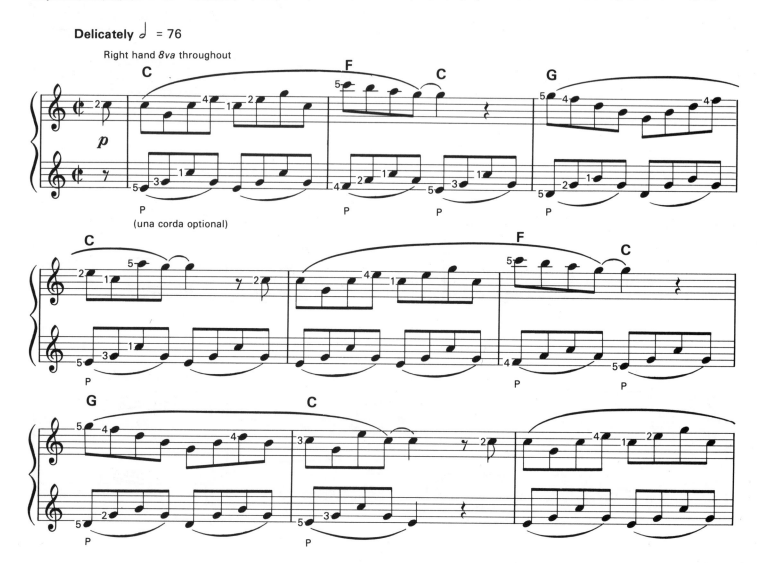

44

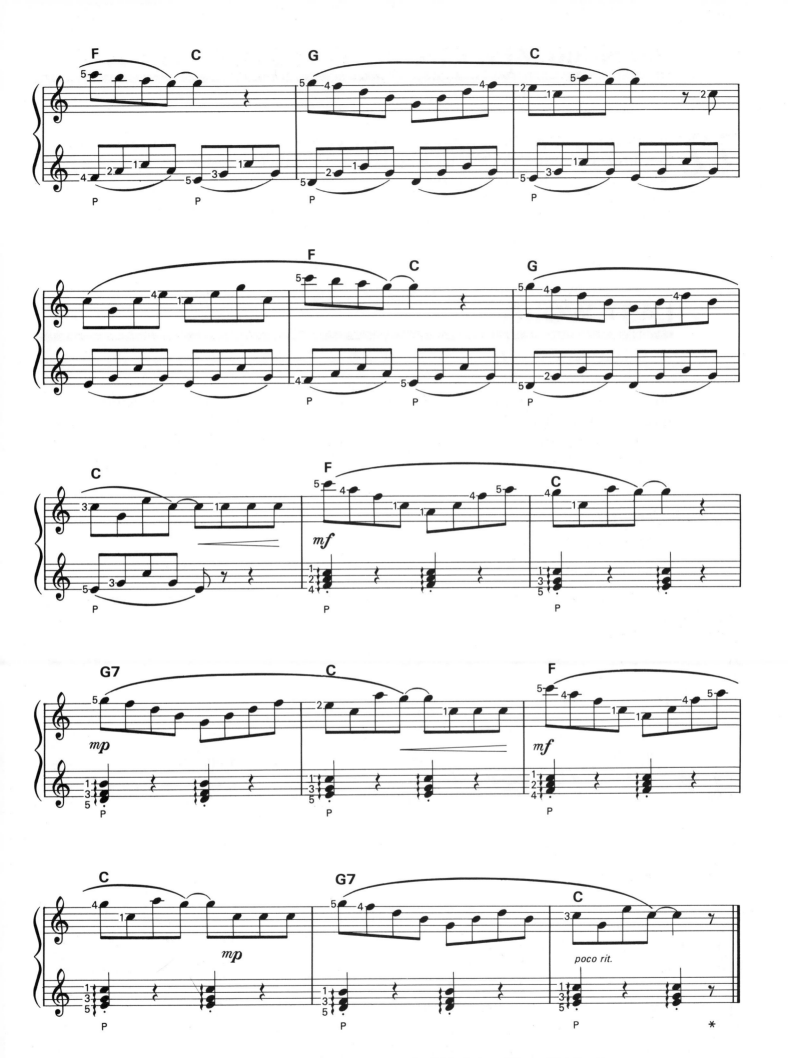

OPEN BROKEN CHORD STYLE FOR LEFT HAND

22 In *Evergreen* your left hand returns again to a 'broken chord' style (see *My Way,* Book Four, page 18, and *Music Box Dancer*, Book Five, page 44). Here in *Evergreen*, however, the chords have been opened up, so the distances you travel will be much greater.

Allow your left wrist to swivel freely from side to side as you encompass the notes.

LAST WORD

So we come to the end of Book Five of 'The Complete Piano Player'. In The Complete Piano Player Style Book you will be studying a number of outstanding piano styles old and new, including: 'Boogie Woogie', 'Blues', 'Shearing Block Chords', 'Country Style', and 'Rock'.

In the meantime here is *Evergreen*:

EVERGREEN

Words: Paul Williams. Music: Barbra Streisand

One _____ love that is shared by two
Time _____ we've learned to sail a-bove

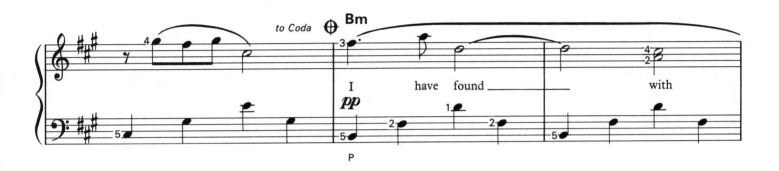

I have found _____ with

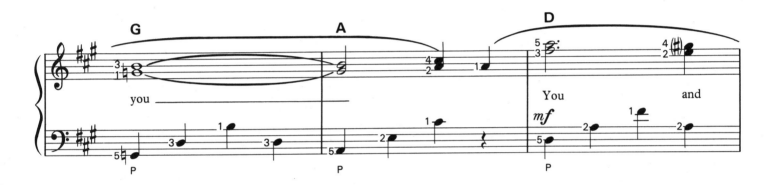

you _____

You and

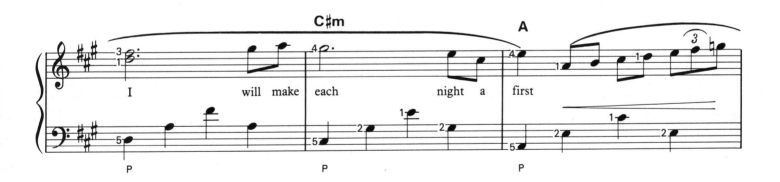

I will make each night a first

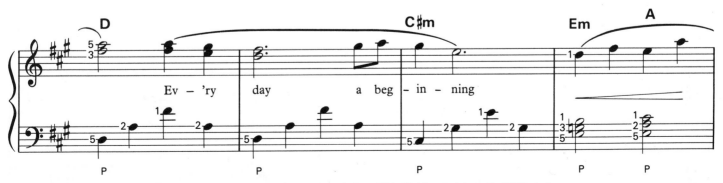

Ev—'ry day a beg—in—ning

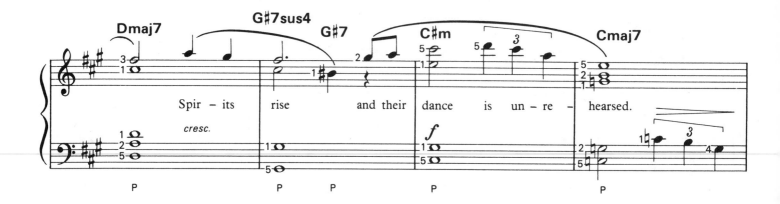

Spir – its rise and their dance is un – re – hearsed.

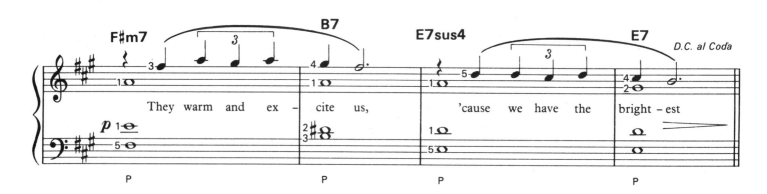

They warm and ex – cite us, 'cause we have the bright – est

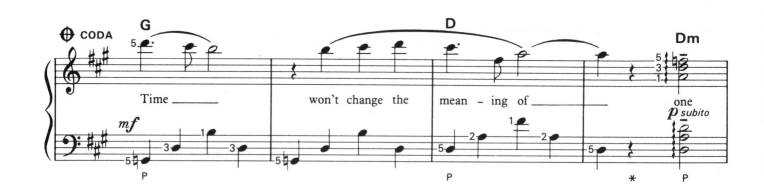

Time _____ won't change the mean – ing of _____ one

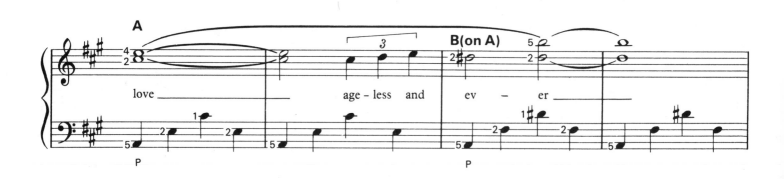

love _____ age – less and ev – er _____

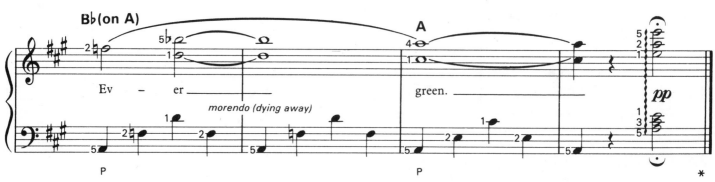

Ev – er _____ green. _____

morendo (dying away)

6/04 (51582)